DATE DUE

OCT 23 '69	JUL 26 '73	DEC 26 '74	
DEC 18	NOV 1 '73		DEC 28 1994
JAN 22 '70	DEC 20 '73		FEB 1 8 199
DEC 24 '70	DEC 27 '73	DEC 13 '78	MAR 20 1996
12 GT '70	JAN 31 '74	DEC 18 '80	DEC 1 2 199
MAY 20 '71	FEB 21 '74	SEP 3 '81	JAN 0 3 1996
AUG 19 '71	JUL 18 '74	DEC 29 '83	DEC 1 8 199
OCT 14 '71	SEP 26 '74	JAN 5 '84	MAR 0 5 1997
JAN 25 '73	DEC 15 '74	APR 26 '84	AUG 2 7 1997
MAY 24 '73	OCT 2 '75	JAN 03 '8	OCT 2 9 1997
OCT 18 '73	NOV 8 '75	JAN 03 '8	NOV 1 7 1997
JAN 12 '78	APR 15 '76	DEC 3 0 199	DEC 0 4 1997
MAY 25 '78	JUL 12 '78		

The story of the first Christmas
Illustrated by Celestino Piatti

The Holy Night

Text by Aurel von Jüchen
Translated from the German
by Cornelia Schaeffer
Atheneum New York 1968

The Holy Night

Everyone in Nazareth was at work.
The men were busy in the fields.
Mothers were cooking lunch.
Only the children were free to play in the streets.

So the children were the first to see a man on a proud horse
    come riding into town.
He was colorfully and splendidly dressed.
The children ran to see and admire him close up.
Then the men and women saw him, too, and came into the street,
    for they were just as curious as the children.

When everyone was in the town marketplace, the man on the horse spoke.

"People of Nazareth," he said, "do you know who I am?"

"No," they answered. "We have no idea.

It is not often that we see so splendid a horseman."

The horseman said, "I am a messenger of Caesar Augustus,

your ruler and the ruler of many lands.

Caesar wants to know how many people live in his kingdoms.

So he wants everyone to be counted.

For this counting, each man must travel to the place where his ancestors lived.

There he must give his name to an official."

When Joseph heard this he said,

"It is not a good time for me to go away.

I am the only carpenter in Nazareth, and there is much work to be done."

When Mary, his wife, heard this, she said,

"It is not a good time for me to go away. My baby will soon be born.

What will happen if he is born on the journey?"

But Caesar had commanded. Everyone had to do what he said.

Joseph packed what they would need for the trip in a blue cloth.
He made a second bundle of hay and oats for the donkey.
And the three of them started off toward Bethlehem,
    for that was where Joseph's family had once lived.

Their road led across the whole country.
They climbed high mountains and went down steep paths.
They traveled for many days.
Vultures screeched in the forests, and jackals howled.
Often Mary sighed softly, "How I wish we were already there."
And Joseph prayed that they would arrive safely.

When they finally did arrive in Bethlehem,
    their feet hurt and they were very tired.
But where would they sleep?
They didn't know anyone who lived there.
Joseph knocked on many doors.
"Good people, take us in," he said. "Please, take us in."
But from everywhere came the same answer:
    "We can't. Impossible. We haven't a place in our house."
Night began to fall. It grew bitterly cold.
Mary and Joseph at last found a little stable
    that lay back from the road.
    It was at least a shelter.

Inside the stable they found everything they needed.
The donkey found fragrant hay that would satisfy his hunger.
Joseph found a lantern.
He lit it and hung it from one of the rafters.
Mary found a manger. She made it into a bed for a baby.
Then, there in that stable, in the middle of the night,
 Mary's child, Jesus, was born.
Mary laid him in the manger and covered him with clothes she had brought
 and with hay, so he wouldn't be cold.

This happened deep in the dark night,
    when all the houses in Bethlehem had long been silent
    and everyone was asleep in his bed.
The only people still awake were a few shepherds
    watching over their sheep on a hill near the town.
They huddled about a fire and warmed their hands.
Suddenly a bright light shone above their heads.

"Where does that light come from?" cried the shepherds,
   throwing themselves down upon the ground in fear.
A song seemed to be coming from the light.
So at last the shepherds looked up
   to see that the whole sky was full of singing angels.
A tall angel stood before them.
"What has happened?" cried the shepherds.
The angel answered, "Christ is born tonight.
   When he is grown, he will make unhappy people happy and sad people glad,
   and he will make the wicked good.
   Go down to Bethlehem and greet your saviour."

When the shepherds heard this,
  they ran as fast as they could down to Bethlehem.

At the door of the stable they looked in,
   and then they stepped inside.
Wide-eyed, they looked at the child in the manger.
In wonder, they knelt down and said,
   "We thank you for coming to make the unhappy happy and the sad cheerful
   and to make all men good."

After the shepherds had looked at the baby for a while,
    they felt they must go out and share their joy.
They said to everyone they met –
    their relatives, their friends, everybody –
    "Do you know that a saviour is born?
    We have seen him. He is here in Bethlehem, in a stable."
So God made the shepherds the first earthly messengers of His love.
In time their message spread to all countries,
    and to children everywhere,
    and so to us.